Winnie the Pooh

How Do You Hop So High?

Something very peculiar was happening in the Hundred-Acre Wood.
Tigger wasn't moving!
"Are you sure that's Tigger?" Roo asked Pooh.
"Well," said Pooh, "it certainly looks like Tigger."
"Yes, but he isn't acting like Tigger," said Roo.

At that moment, Tigger noticed his friends. He held his finger to his lips.

"Come over here on your tippiest tippity-toes, Buddy Boys," he whispered. "I want to show you something amazifying!"

"Look!" Tigger said quietly, pointing to a spot on the ground.

"I don't see anything," said Roo.

"You have to stay very still and look very closely," said Tigger.

"Oh!" shouted Roo. "Oh, I see it! It's a frog!"

At Roo's shout, the frog hopped high into the air and kept hopping until it was out of sight.

"Oops!" said Roo. "Sorry, Tigger. I didn't mean to scare him away."

"That's okay," Tigger said. "Did you see how high that little fella could hop?"

Roo nodded. "I can hop high, too," he said. "Watch!"

"Hopping is what tiggers do best," said Tigger. "Look!"

"What about you, Pooh?" called Roo.

But when Pooh tried to hop, his feet hardly got off the ground.

"How do you hop so high?" asked Pooh.

"It's easy when you have a spring in your tail," said Tigger.

"Or big, bouncy feet," said Roo.

"Or sproingy frog-type legs," said Tigger.

"I guess I just wasn't made for hopping," said Pooh, looking at his springless, sproingless self.

"Guess what else I saw when I was sitting still and observerating?" Tigger said. "You'll never guess. Can you guess? I saw a fish!"

"Where?" asked Pooh, looking around.

"In the pond," Tigger said. "Over there."

"Maybe if we wait quietly, it will come back," Roo said hopefully.

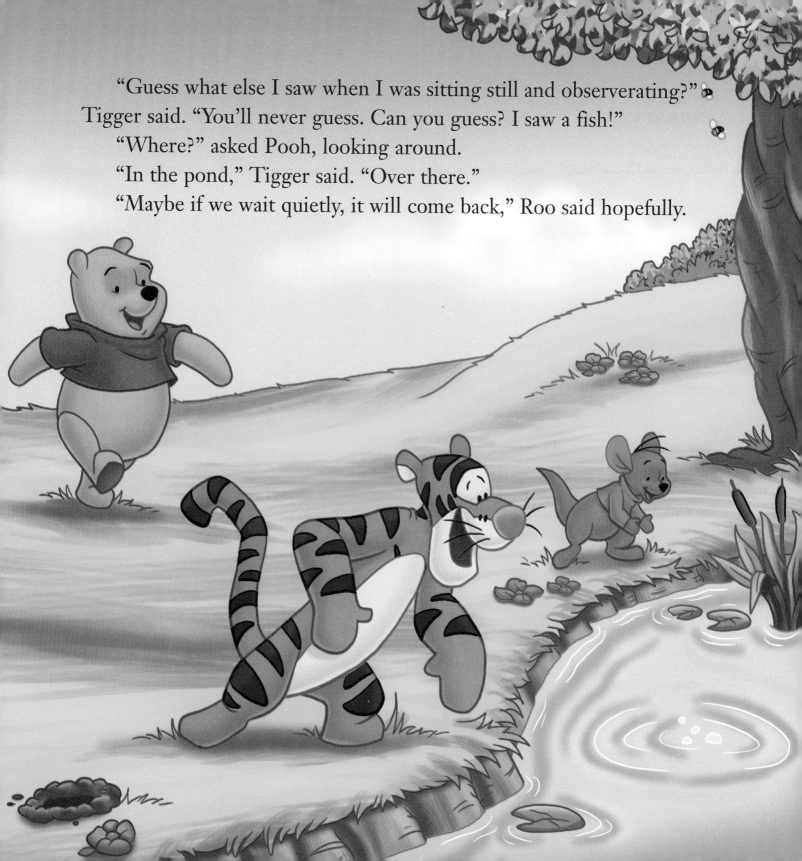

So the three friends settled onto the grassy shore of the pond to watch and listen. Soon Pooh was snoring gently. Roo fidgeted and twitched. "It's awfully hard to sit still and be patient, isn't it, Tigger?" Roo whispered.

"It sure is," Tigger agreed. "But if you stick with it, you start to notice wunnerful things. Like dandelion fuzzies floating in the sunshine, and shy little chirp-chirp sounds in the trees."

"And—oh, look, Tigger!" Roo said excitedly. "A fish in the pond!"

Tigger woke Pooh, and the three friends watched the fish splash and swim through the water.

"How do fish learn to swim underwater?" Pooh asked.

"I don't know," said Roo. "I can't even put my head under the water."

"Swimming underwater is what tiggers do best,"
Tigger said. "I'll show you!"

Tigger dove into the pond and came up sputtering.

"I suppose I might have been an even better underwater swimmer
if I'd been born a fish," he said.

Tigger lay down in the sun to dry, soggy and shivering.
He soon found himself eye to eye with a brown squirrel.
Quick as a flash, the squirrel grabbed an acorn on the
ground next to Tigger and hightailed it up the nearest tree.
"How do squirrels climb like that?" asked Roo.

"Hoo-hoo-hoo! I'll show you!" Tigger cried. "Climbing is what tiggers do best."

Tigger scrambled up onto a branch of the tree—and got stuck there.

"On second thought," he called down to his friends, "maybe climbing is what squirrels do best—and tiggers do second-best."

Suddenly Tigger noticed a nest on his branch.

"It's filled with baby birds!" he said.

"And it looks like one of them is going to try to fly!" Pooh said.

The friends watched in amazement as the tiny bird fluttered its wings—and flew into the air!

"How do baby birds learn to fly?" Roo asked.

"It just so happens that flying is what tiggers do best," Tigger said. "But," he added, looking down at the ground from his perch in the tree, "tiggers don't like to fly nearly as much as birds do...."

"Isn't it amazing what different animals can do?" Roo asked after he and Pooh helped Tigger down from the tree.

"Some can hop, and some can swim," said Tigger.

"Some can climb, and some can fly," said Roo.

"I'm not good at any of those things," Pooh said sadly. "Are there any other special hopping, swimming, climbing, flying things to choose from?" he asked hopefully.

"Let's go observerating and find out!" Tigger said. "Come on, Buddy Boys!"

Stopping often to look and listen, the friends discovered lots of different animals with special talents. They saw ducks gliding on the water and a beaver building a dam. They saw a gopher digging a hole and a bee collecting pollen.

They were nearing Rabbit's garden when a fast-moving blur rushed past. It was Rabbit. He was rushing to chase a bird away from his newly planted seeds.

"How do you run so fast?" Pooh asked when they finally caught up.

Rabbit shrugged. "It's a rabbit thing, I guess," he said.

"It would be a tigger thing, too, if it didn't tire me out so much," said Tigger.

Just then, Eeyore came by, carrying a heavy load of sticks.

"How do you carry so much, Eeyore?" asked Pooh.

"I'm really strong," said Eeyore. "Carrying things is easy for me."

"For me, too," said Tigger, struggling to juggle several skinny sticks.

"I didn't know until today that you had so many talents, Tigger!" said Roo.

"Hoo-hoo-hoo! There's not much a tigger *can't* do!" cried Tigger.

Pooh sighed. "I'm afraid there's not much that a fluffy-headed bear like me *can* do," he said.

"Not so, Buddy Boy!" Tigger cried. "Everybody has talents of his own."

"Maybe if I go to my Thinking Spot, I'll be able to figure out what my special talent is," said Pooh.

"We'll help you, Pooh," said Roo.

"Yeah! Thinking is what tiggers do best," Tigger said.

So the three friends went to Pooh's Thinking Spot to think.
"I have an idea!" Tigger said. "Let's draw a chart to reminderize
ourselves of all of the different animals and talents we've seen today."
But when they finished filling in the chart, Pooh's spot was still blank.
"See?" said Pooh. "I'm not good at any of those things."

"Maybe not," said Tigger. "But you're the best tummy-bouncer in the Hundred-Acre Wood!"

"Yes! And I've never met anyone with a better nose for honey," said Roo. "You can smell honey from miles away, Pooh."

"We haven't even mentioned your most special-est talent of all," said Tigger. "And that's your talent for friendship, Pooh!"

Then Tigger drew a picture of a big puffy heart—right under Pooh's name on the talent chart.

What Are Your Special Talents?

Every living thing has talents and abilities that make it special. In many cases, an animal's talents help it survive in a particular place. Fish swim and breathe underwater, so they have special talents to live in ponds, lakes, rivers, and oceans. Squirrels can climb trees where they find food and shelter. Beavers can cut down trees to build their own homes.

All animals—from tiny protozoa, too small for us to see, to the biggest whales swimming in the sea—are born with unique natural abilities that help make them what they are and shape how they live.

Young children learn through observing, comparing, and creating. Use the following to help your child learn more about animals' special talents.

Step 1: Sit quietly and observe. Do you see any animals using their special talents?

Step 2: Tigger, Pooh, and Roo compared themselves to the other animals in the story. How do your talents compare to the ones in the story?

Step 3: Make your own talent chart with a piece of paper and some markers. Draw a grid like the one Tigger drew on page 25. Fill in animals and friends that you've observed. What are their special talents? Don't forget to include yourself—just make sure the box on the chart is big enough to hold all of your special abilities!